The Christmas Tree Cried

by Claudia Cangilla McAdam

illustrated by Anna-Maria L. Crum

To Your Grandkids—
May the Spirit of
Christmas be with
you every day
of the year!
Claudia Cangilla McAdam

Two Sons Press, Inc.
Highlands Ranch, Colorado

For Gary, Brian, and Kevin—you are a trio of blessings in my life. —C.C.M.

For Uncle Jimmy—you're always ready with a helping hand
and a shoulder to lean on. —A.L.C.

For valuable assistance and information, I must thank Pam Helmsing, Assistant Director of the National Christmas Tree Association, and several individuals from the White House: Chief Usher Gary Walters, Chief Floral Designer Nancy Clarke, and Photo Editor Lynden Steele. For guidance and support, I also thank Maria Downs and William Bushong of the White House Historical Association, Nancy Crowley, Dale Duxbury, Kitty Kolody, Sharon Linowski, Alison Lusk, Elizabeth Nelson, Floyd Edward Reinhardt, Sonya Sharp, and the members of my writers critique group. Special appreciation goes to Home & Garden Television for the inspiration for this book provided by their HGTV *White House Christmas* specials. —C.C.M.

Two Sons Press, Inc.
14 Red Tail Drive
Highlands Ranch, CO 80126
303-346-3003
www.twosonspress.com

CURRENT PRINTING (last digit)
10 9 8 7 6 5 4 3 2 1

ISBN # 0-9748995-5-0
Library of Congress Control Number: 2004090420

Publisher's Cataloging-in-Publication Data

McAdam, Claudia Cangilla.
  The Christmas Tree Cried by Claudia Cangilla McAdam ; illustrations by Anna-Maria L. Crum.
  32 p.: col. ill.; 26 cm.

Summary: A giant conifer desires nothing more than to be chosen as someone's Christmas tree, but after being rejected time and again and facing fears of the lumber mill when it is finally cut down, the tree finds itself as the holiday centerpiece of the country's most important home.
ISBN 0-9748995-5-0

1.Christmas-Juvenile. 2. Christmas trees-United States-Washington, D.C.
3. Trees-Folklore. 4. Christmas trees-History.

PZ8.3.M123Ch 2004

The illustrations for this book were done in watercolor on Fabriano Uno soft 140 lb. watercolor paper.

Tucked in a tree farm so silent and deep
A giant conifer started to weep,
For the season had arrived once again
When stars sing praise and hills echo "Amen!"

The tree knew that soon the farm would be full
As families in scarves and mittens of wool
Crunched boots through new snow with high hopes to find
A fragrant Christmas tree, one of a kind.

A pine tree, a spruce, or maybe a fir
With a scent as sweet as the gift of myrrh
Marking the birth of a Savior and King
And the start of a reign everlasting.

The conifer struggled all its life long
To grow up beautiful, tall, straight, and strong,
Stretching long boughs like arms begging its plea
That it be chosen as a Christmas tree.

But year after year the tree was passed by,
And after some thought, it understood why.
It had grown so big, it had to admit—
There wasn't a room in which it could fit.

"Too tall, too thick," is what people would say.
"We can't get it home; there's really no way."
"Too bushy, too heavy,—it's much too wide!"
With each rejection, the conifer cried.

And so it all happened again this year—
A snowflake was formed with every new tear
As slicing the cold came shouts of sheer glee—
"Please hurry, come look—I've found the best tree!"

The giant was never the one preferred,
And so much snow fell, the scene became blurred
As families chose spruces laden with cones,
Soft firs and fine pines whose boughs had "good bones."

The conifer found it so hard to cope,
A whispered prayer seemed the tree's only hope:
A child of the earth, the Christmas tree,
Makes a gift of itself, oh Lord, to Thee.

Sign of endless life, branches ever green,
Wood of peace pointing toward heaven unseen.
Let me bring honor and Your sign of grace
To worthy people in a special place.

One frosty day, the wind cut like a sword,
And through the thin air, a truck engine roared.
Farm workers! That thought struck the tree with fear.
Old wood and thick brush they've come here to clear.

Tires etching deep tracks shot up sprays of snow,
Stopped at the conifer, wouldn't you know,
And out jumped two men with measuring rods.
Had they come for this tree? What were the odds?

It measured eighteen full feet...and a half.
The two men nodded, then started to laugh.
"You're out of here, pal," the tree heard one state,
And a chain saw sealed the conifer's fate.

Fly
Casting
Make molds
of your
favorite bugs

Bound up like a mummy, boughs tucked in tight,
The truck pulled it out through the fading light.
Placed on a flatbed, wrapped up in the chill,
Destined, most certain, for the logger's mill.

Hugging hilly highways, banking through curves,
The conifer bounced, a bundle of nerves.
How long would it take? How far would they go?
When would the end come? It wanted to know.

Gas, Food,
Lodging
Next Exit

Mom's
Pies
Good for
Smelling,
Eating, &
Throwing

Piggy Savings

Where Banking Makes Cents.

The tree sped along, it seemed like it flew
Through the following day and evening, too.
Black draped the skies when the truck finally stopped;
Sure that this was the end, the tree's heart dropped.

It had tried so hard, as hard as it could
To be a Christmas tree, not milled for wood.
It grew big and strong, and this was its thanks—
To be shaved and planed and sliced into planks?

How could this be an answer to a prayer?
Wasn't anyone listening way up there?
But a flicker of faith was fanned, it seems—
A thread of trust tied the tree to its dreams.

Then it was pulled through a wide double door
And came to rest on a smooth, shiny floor.
This was the mill?—that thought became garbled—
Since when was the floor polished and marbled?

Pulleys and ropes and a plan rather grand
Set the righted tree in a metal stand.
The ties were cut, the conifer unbound,
And its boughs swung free with a swishing sound.

Crowned with a halo of soft, amber light
The tree observed an astonishing sight—
Circled by people, the conifer saw
Faces of wonder, mouths opened in awe.

The hush gave way to murmurs of pleasure—
"Perfect." "The best." "A national treasure!"
The spell was broken as chaos ensued:
"Let's dress up this tree—it's standing here nude."

Scaffolding stretched to the tree's tallest heights
As hands gently tucked in miniature lights.
Garlands of golden beads draped outstretched limbs,
Branches dressed up with all sorts of trims.

Ornaments, hand-made, and shiny glass balls
Bounced pinpoints of light off each of the walls.
A thick velvet skirt wrapped 'round the tree's base,
A royal carpet, a soft touch of grace.

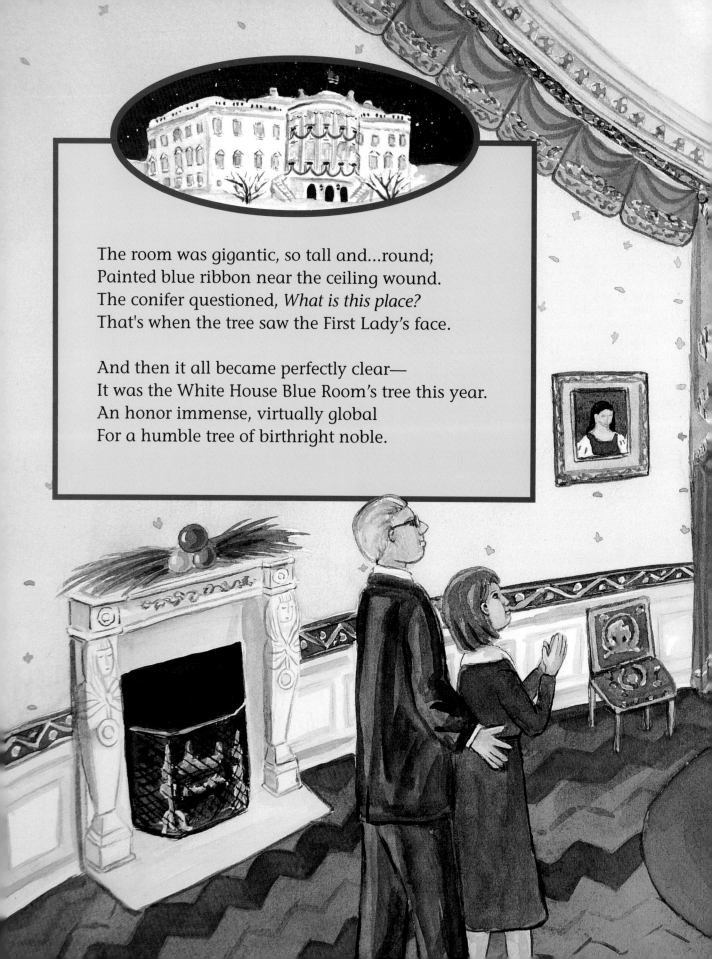

The room was gigantic, so tall and...round;
Painted blue ribbon near the ceiling wound.
The conifer questioned, *What is this place?*
That's when the tree saw the First Lady's face.

And then it all became perfectly clear—
It was the White House Blue Room's tree this year.
An honor immense, virtually global
For a humble tree of birthright noble.

Prayers more than answered, to reach this station
As the Christmas tree for the whole nation
With duties that now became crystal clear—
Spreading yuletide joy and holiday cheer.

Gratitude shone in the President's eyes;
The conifer never dreamt such a prize.
Thrilled and quite thankful, filled up with pure pride,
So happy indeed—the Christmas tree cried.

About the Story

While *The Christmas Tree Cried* is a made-up story about the tree that is selected for the Blue Room in the White House, there are many parts of the story that are based on facts. For example, the tree selected for the Blue Room must, indeed, be $18\frac{1}{2}$-feet tall. You'll discover why that's so in the section that follows.

Also, the prayer that the conifer offers up on the farm is based on the words of the eighth-century missionary St. Boniface who brought Christianity to Germany. One Christmas Eve, he came upon the son of a chieftain who was soon to be sacrificed to pagan gods. The place of the sacrifice was under a giant oak, considered sacred to the gods. To prove these gods powerless, Boniface amazed the people by felling the tree with a single stroke of an ax.

Pointing to an evergreen tree, Boniface said, "This little tree, a young child of the forest, shall be a home tree tonight. It is the wood of peace, for your houses are built of fir. It is the sign of endless life, for its branches are ever green. See how it points toward heaven? Let this be called the tree of the Christ child. Gather about it, not in the wild woods, but in your homes. There it will shelter no deeds of blood, but loving gifts and lights of kindness."

And so the Christmas tree was born.

How the Blue Room Tree is Chosen

Courtesy National Christmas Tree Association

The search for the Christmas tree that will adorn the Blue Room in the White House begins months ahead of time.

The people who grow Christmas trees as a business belong to an organization called the National Christmas Tree Association. Every other year, they have a convention where they hold a Christmas tree contest.

Growers bring sample trees, and association members vote on which tree is the best. The top two vote-getters win the honor of presenting the White House with a tree for the Blue Room—one for the current year, the other for the next year.

Back at the tree farm, the winning grower identifies two or three trees which would be appropriate for the Blue Room. A team from the White House comes to the farm in the fall and picks the tree that will find a home in the Blue Room.

The tree must be 18 feet, 6 inches tall because it needs to fit perfectly from the floor to the 18$\frac{1}{2}$-foot high ceiling in that room. Each year, the chandelier in the Blue Room is removed, and the tree is attached to the chandelier support to give it stability. The electrical connection in the ceiling is then used to power the lights on the tree.

The tree is delivered to the White House grounds a day or two before the official presentation. On the big day, it is loaded onto a large green wooden wagon pulled by a team of horses. The tree journeys up the walk to the White House where it is presented to the First Lady.

Courtesy National Christmas Tree Association

The furniture in the Blue Room is removed, and the floors are covered to protect them. The tree is brought in and placed into a large stand that holds 20 gallons of water. Since the branches have been bundled up, the tree is allowed to "settle" for a few hours before the decorating begins. Then the designers take over. Months earlier, the First Lady decided on a theme for the Christmas decorations. Frequently, different organizations or states produce ornaments in keeping with the theme.

The next two to four days are a flurry of activity. Scaffolding is brought in so decorators can reach the tree's heights. Sometimes the branches are reinforced with wire to provide extra strength for the hundreds of decorations. The lights are strung, and depending on how bushy the tree is, there might be 8,000 lights on it!

White House photo by Tina Hager

White House photo by Susan Sterner

Throughout the White House, wreaths grace the windows, swags drape across fireplace mantles, and garlands of greenery snake up stairways. Freshly-cut evergreen trees placed in other rooms fill the house with the scent of Christmas.

In the Blue Room, when the final ornament is hung and the last garland strung, the scaffolding is removed, the protective floor is taken up, and the tree is ready to be admired.

Throughout the holidays, the elegant Blue Room tree greets dignitaries, visitors, and viewers of White House Christmas television specials with the beauty and majesty befitting it as the honored centerpiece of the miracle on Pennsylvania Avenue.

A History of Christmas Trees in the White House

There haven't always been Christmas trees in the White House. In fact, the nation didn't even *have* a White House until 1800. Through the years, trees have become an important part of Christmas celebrations. Here are some of the highlights:

1889: During the Benjamin Harrison administration, the first Christmas tree in the White House was placed in the second floor Yellow Oval Room, which was used as a family parlor and library at the time. It was decorated with candles and toys for the Harrison grandchildren.

1895: First Lady Frances Cleveland hung the first electric lights on the White House tree. Electricity had come to the White House in 1891.

1902: Theodore Roosevelt didn't believe in cutting down trees for Christmas, but his children snuck a Christmas tree into the White House, decorated it, and hid it in a big closet. When President Roosevelt found out, he let them keep it. After he learned that cutting down Christmas trees helped forests thrive, the Roosevelts had a small tree in the White House each year.

1909: The Taft children placed the Christmas tree in the Blue Room for the first time.

1929: Starting this year with First Lady Lou Hoover, the honor of trimming the principle White House Christmas tree has been held by every subsequent First Lady.

1953: The Eisenhowers topped all previous First Families in the number of trees filling every floor of the White House: 26.

1961: Beginning with the Kennedys, themes have been selected each year for the Blue Room tree. The first theme in 1961 featured characters and toys from the ballet "Nutcracker Suite."

1966: The National Christmas Tree Association held its first competition to provide the Blue Room tree.

2001: George and Laura Bush's Christmas White House boasted 49 trees—a new record!

About the Author

When Claudia Cangilla McAdam began writing poetry as a child, she decided she wanted to be a professional writer when she grew up. For more than twenty-five years, her fiction, nonfiction and poetry have appeared in scores of magazines and newspapers. Photography is one of her hobbies, and her pictures accompany much of her written work. She is the co-author of seven books including two nonfiction book series for the children's educational market: *Heroic Acts* and *Portraits of Character*. The parents of two grown sons, Claudia and her husband live in Highlands Ranch, Colorado. From their deck, the view of the Rocky Mountains is a constant reminder of all the Christmas trees, big and small, that grow nearby.

Photo by Dale Duxbury

About the Illustrator

Photo by Hilari Bell

Anna-Maria L. Crum lives with her dog, Buster, a mile down the road from Claudia, although she doesn't have her view. She has to lean out on her balcony and look between two buildings to see the Rockies. But she is inspired every day by the gorgeous blue Colorado sky. She's written 12 and illustrated over 20 children's books. When she works too long, Buster dances by her drawing table asking her to come play. He usually succeeds.

Books Make Great Gifts

To order a copy of *The Christmas Tree Cried*, send $16.95 plus $4.50 shipping and handling. (Colorado residents add $.80 tax.) Make check or money order payable to Two Sons Press, Inc. Send your name, address, phone number, and e-mail address along with the payment to:

Two Sons Press, Inc.
14 Red Tail Drive
Highlands Ranch, CO 80126

For multiple books or credit card orders:
Telephone 303-346-3003 or fax 303-791-2226
Toll free 1-888-TWO-SONS (1-888-896-7667)

www.twosonspress.com